Spring Harvest Praise 2001

Equipping the Church for action

Copyright and photocopying

Acknowledgements
Scripture quotations taken from the HOLY BIBLE, NEW INTERNATIONAL VERSION.
Copyright ©1973, 1978, 1984 by International Bible Society. Used by permission of Hodder and Stoughton Limited. All rights reserved. "NIV" is a registered trade mark of International Bible Society. UK trademark number 1448790
Common Worship: Services and Prayers for the Church of England (Church House Publishing, 2000) material from which is included in this book is copyright © The Archbishops' Council 2000 and is reproduced by permission.

Spring Harvest wishes to acknowledge and thank the following people for their help in the compilation and production of this songbook: Pat Bilbrough, Trine Crouch, Deborah Lugg, David Peacock, Sue Rinaldi, Adrian Thompson, Cheryl Williams and Spring Harvest Head Office staff. Thank you to Christopher Cocksworth, Jonathan Cushnie, Mark Earey, Jane Reeves, Paul Sheppy, Northumbria Community Trust and Fiona Williamson for liturgy contributions.

Layout by Spring Harvest
Cover design by Adept Design
Printed in the UK by Halcyon

Published by Spring Harvest, 14 Horsted Square, Uckfield, East Sussex, TN22 1QL, UK.
Spring Harvest. A Registered Charity.
Distributed by ICC, Silverdale Road, Eastbourne, East Sussex, BN20 7AB, UK.

ISBN 1 899 78838 7

Spring Harvest Praise 2001

1
A PURPLE ROBE

a crown of thorn, a reed in his right hand;
before the soldiers' spite and scorn
I see my Saviour stand.

He bears between the Roman guard
the weight of all our woes;
a stumbling figure bowed and scarred
I see my Saviour go.

Fast to the cross's spreading span,
high in sun lit air,
all the un-numbered sins of man
I see my Saviour bear.

He hangs, by whom the world was made,
beneath the darkened sky;
the everlasting ransom paid,
I see my Saviour die.

He shares on high his Father's throne,
who once in mercy came;
for all his love to sinners shown
I sing my Saviour's name.

Words copyright © Timothy Dudley-Smith

1a The servant King
Matthew 20:28

... the Son of Man did not come
to be served, but to serve,
and to give his life as a ransom for many.

2
ALL THE WAY, MY SAVIOUR LEADS ME

what have I to ask beside?
Can I doubt his tender mercy,
who through life has been my guide?
Heavenly peace, divinest comfort,
here by faith in him to dwell,
for I know whate'er befall me,
Jesus doeth all things well.

All the way, my Saviour leads me,
cheers each winding path I tread.
Gives me grace for ev'ry trial,
feeds me with the living bread.
Though my weary steps may falter
and my soul athirst may be,
gushing from a Rock before me
Lo! A spring of joy I see.

All the way, my Saviour leads me,
oh the fullness of his love.
Perfect rest to me is promised
in my Father's house above.
When my spirit clothed immortal
wings it's flight to realms of day,
this my song through endless ages,
Jesus led me all the way.

Fanny Crosby

2a Blessing

See that ye be at peace among yourselves,
my children, and love one another.
Follow the example of good men of old
and God will comfort you and help you,
both in this world
and in the world which is to come.

'Columba's prayer' (Blessing in Evening Prayer from Celtic Daily Prayer) © Northumbria Community Trust Ltd, Tel: 01289 388235

3
AMAZING GRACE

how sweet the sound
that saved a wretch like me;
I once was lost, but now am found,
was blind, but now I see.

Amazing love has come to me.
I lift up my voice to the heavens,
lift up my hands to the King,
and I cry 'hosanna, hosanna in the highest.'
Jesus my Lord is exalted far above every name,
and I cry 'hosanna, hosanna in the highest.'

'Twas grace that taught my heart to fear,
and grace my fears relieved;
how precious did that grace appear,
the hour I first believed!

The Lord has promised good to me,
his word my hope secures;
he will my shield and portion be
as long as life endures.

When we've been there a thousand years,
bright shining as the sun,
we've no less days to sing God's praise
than when we first begun.

John Newton (1725-1807). Adpt. Nathan Fellingham
Copyright © 2000 Kingsway's Thankyou Music

4

AS WE COME TODAY

we remind ourselves of what we do;
that these songs are not just songs,
but signs of love for you.
This is a holy moment now,
something of heaven touches earth,
voices of angels all resound,
we join their song.

Come, come, come, let us worship God
with our hands held high,
and our hearts bowed down.
We will run, run, run through your gates, O God,
with a shout of love, with a shout of love.

Lord, with confidence
we come before your throne of grace.
Not that we deserve to come
but you have paid the way.
You are the holy King of all,
heaven and earth are in your hands,
all of the angels sing your song,
we join them now.

Matt Redman
Copyright © 2000 Kingsway's Thankyou Music

5

BELOVÈD AND BLESSÈD

the Father's pure delight.
Redeemer, sustainer
you're my passion and my prize.

My brother, my comforter,
my Shepherd and my friend.
My ransom, my righteousness,
you're the stream that never ends.

You're unchanging, you're magnificent
you are all I could desire.
You're my breath of life,
sun of righteousness,
you're the love that satisfies.

There's kindness, compassion
for those who will draw near;
acceptance, forgiveness,
and a love that conquers fear.

You're the Word of life,
you're the Bread of heaven,
you're the Lion and the Lamb.
All within me cries, 'Lord be glorified
by everything I am'.
Belovèd, my belovèd.

Stuart Townend
Copyright © 2000 Kingsway's Thankyou Music

6

BLESS THE LORD, O MY SOUL

and all that is within me.
Bless the Lord, O my soul
and all that is within me
bless his holy name, bless his holy name.

He is good, good to us
and his love endures forever.
He is good, good to us
and his love endures forever.
Bless his holy name, bless his holy name.

Open wide heaven's gates,
let the King of glory in.
Open wide heaven's gates,
let the King of glory in.
Bless his holy name, bless his holy name.

Godfrey Birtill
Copyright © 2000 Radical UK Music/Sovereign Music UK

6a Prayer of blessing

May the Father of Life
pour out His grace on you;
may you feel His hand in everything you do
and be strengthened by the things
He brings you through:
this is my prayer for you.

May the Son of God be Lord in all your ways;
and may He shepherd you the length
of all your days,
and in your heart may He receive the praise:
this is my prayer for you.

And despite how simple it may sound,
I pray that His grace will abound
and motivate everything you do;
and may the fullness of His love
be shared through you.

May His Spirit comfort you,
and make you strong,
may He discipline you gently
when you're wrong,
and in your heart may He give you a song:
this is my prayer for you.

May Jesus be Lord in all your ways,
may He shepherd you
the length of all your days,
and in your heart may He receive the praise:
this is my prayer for you.

'My prayer for you' from Celtic Daily Prayer
© Northumbria Community Trust. Tel: 01289 388235

7
BLESSED ARE THE HUMBLE SOULS
who see their emptiness and poverty;
treasures of grace to them are giv'n:
the kingdom of their God in heav'n.

Blessed are the mourners, grieved in heart
that inward sin will not depart;
the blood of Christ for cleansing flows,
a comfort for their deepest woes.

Blessed are the meek, whose gentle strength
will bring them great rewards at length;
for God who gave them second birth
shall make them heirs of all the earth.

Blessed are the souls who in distress
hunger and thirst for righteousness;
they shall be satisfied, and fed
with living streams and heaven's bread.

Blessed are the merciful, whose love
flows only from its source above;
forgiving are they, gentle, kind:
mercy they show, and mercy find.

Blessed are the pure in heart, and clean
from the defiling powers of sin;
with what delight their eyes will see
their God for all eternity!

Blessed are all those who, making peace,
make hatred, wrong and warfare cease;
they bear one likeness, chosen ones,
and they shall all be called God's sons.

Blessed, all who of great shame partake
for righteousness, for Jesus' sake;
all joy they know, all grace is given;
theirs is the kingdom, theirs is heaven.

Words based on Isaac Watts (1674-1748)
Copyright © in this version Praise Trust

8
BLESSÈD ARE THE POOR
in spirit, for theirs is the kingdom of heav'n.
Blessèd are the mourning hearts,
comfort to them will be giv'n.
Blessèd are the humble and meek,
they will inherit the earth.
Blessèd are those who hunger and thirst
      for righteousness,
for they will be filled.

Rejoice and be glad
for great your reward in heaven.
(Repeat)

Blessèd are the merciful
for mercy to them will be shown.
Blessèd are the pure in heart
for they will see their God.
Blessèd are the makers of peace,
they will be called sons of God.
Blessèd are those who suffer for Christ
      and righteousness,
theirs the kingdom of heav'n.

Give glory to God
for he's our reward in heaven
(Repeat)

David Lyle Morris and Pat Youd
Copyright © 2000 Kingsway's Thankyou Music

9
BY YOUR GRACE
I may come
by the blood of the Lamb
to your throne with confidence,
to worship you.

By your pow'r I am free
from the guilt that covered me.
Now I come in righteousness
to worship you.

Just as I am,
not depending on my righteousness;
all that I have is the blood you shed for me.
So now I come, with a thankful heart,
to worship at your feet ...

... O Lamb of God, I come to you:
O Lamb of God, I come to you.

Copyright © 2000 Matt Ots & Jayne Lewis

10
CELEBRATE IN THE LORD
he is the reason we rejoice;
for he has cast our sins away,
forgotten now, forever and always,
always, always, yes always,
always, always.

This is our jubilee,
no debt, no bondage, we are free.
We're free to give him everything
for we have nothing, now it is all his.
All his, all his, all his,
all his, all his.

continued over...

5

This is where the party is,
this is where the joy of heav'n abounds.
In his presence we are free
to praise, to shout aloud.
This is where the party is,
singing with the angels, hear the sound.
This is where the party is,
we are dancing on holy ground,
holy ground, holy ground, holy ground,
holy ground.

For freedom you have set us free,
no longer bound to slavery,
you've broken every chain that binds;
you've conquered sin forever and all time.
All time, all time, yes all time,
all time, all time.

This is where the party is...

...holy ground

Siyavuya, siyavuya, siyavuya (Repeat)

Jabulani, jabulani, jabulani (Repeat)

Evan Rogers
Copyright © 2000 Kingsway's Thankyou Music

11
DRAWN FROM EVERY TRIBE

ev'ry tongue and nation,
gathered before the throne.
Casting down their crowns, they fall at his feet
and worship the Lord alone.
What a glorious sight, dressed in robes of white,
washed by the blood of the Lamb.
Singing ...

Praise and glory, wisdom and thanks,
honour, power and strength
be to our God, forever
and ever, amen.

We are those who follow,
through scenes of fiery trial,
drawing from wells of grace.
Through the darkest valley,
from the depths of pain,
we'll come to that holy place.
We will overcome by looking to the Lamb
and worshipping face to face.
Singing ...

Praise and glory ...

Never will we hunger, we'll no longer thirst,
there's shade from the heat of day.
Led to springs of life,
Jesus our Shepherd will wipe every tear away.

Our God upon the throne will shelter all his own
who worship him night and day.
Singing ...

Praise and glory ...

All glory and honour and power to Jesus (Repeat)
Forever and ever, and ever, and ever (Repeat)
Amen. (Repeat x2)

David Lyle Morris and Faith Forster
Copyright © 2000 Kingsway's Thankyou Music

11a For giving thanks
Psalm 100

Shout for joy to the Lord, all the earth.
Worship the Lord with gladness;
come before him with joyful songs.
Know that the Lord is God.
It is he who made us, and we are his;
we are his people,
the sheep of his pasture.

Enter his gates with thanksgiving
and his courts with praise;
give thanks to him and praise his name.
For the Lord is good
and his love endures for ever;
his faithfulness continues
through all generations.

12
EMPTY, BROKEN, HERE I STAND

Kyrie eleison.
Touch me with your healing hand - Kyrie eleison.
Take my arrogance and pride - Kyrie eleison.
Wash me in your mercy's tide - Kyrie eleison.
Kyrie eleison, Christe eleison, Kyrie eleison.

When my faith has all but gone - Kyrie eleison.
Give me strength to carry on - Kyrie eleison.
When my dreams have turned to dust - Kyrie eleison.
In you, O Lord, I put my trust - Kyrie eleison.
Kyrie eleison, Christe eleison, Kyrie eleison.

When my heart is cold as ice - Kyrie eleison.
Your love speaks of sacrifice - Kyrie eleison.
Love that sets the captive free - Kyrie eleison.
O pour compassion down on me - Kyrie eleison.
Kyrie eleison, Christe eleison, Kyrie eleison.

You're the voice that calms my fears - Kyrie eleison.
You're the laughter, dries my tears - Kyrie eleison.
You're my music, my refrain - Kyrie eleison.
Help me sing your song again - Kyrie eleison.
Kyrie eleison, Christe eleison, Kyrie eleison.

Humble heart of holiness - Kyrie eleison.
Kiss me with your tenderness - Kyrie eleison.
Jesus, faithful friend and true - Kyrie eleison.
All I am I give to you - Kyrie eleison.
Kyrie eleison, Christe eleison, Kyrie eleison.

13

EVERLASTING

ever true, all creation sings to you.
Ever faithful, living Lord,
let the sound of praise be heard.

Jesus, you are
all that I am living for
and all that I believe is in you.
Jesus, all that I am living for
and all that I believe is in you.

Never changing, awesome God,
sing the glory of the Lord.
Ever loving, holy One,
I will praise what you have done.

14

EVERYTHING I AM

and ev'rything I have I give to you.
Ev'rything I want and ev'rything I dream
I give to you.

'Cos you are,
you are ev'rything to me
'Cos you are,
you are ev'rything to me.

Take me on a journey
into your heart.
Take me on a journey
into your love.

14a Thomas' declaration
Based on John 20:28

We see the risen Christ and declare with
Thomas;

'My Lord and my God!'

15

FATHER, TO YOU

with songs of love we come,
into your presence, in awe of all you've done;
brought here with joy, before your throne of grace,
and, in the Son you love, given our place.

What grace to be found in him,
heaven's glorious King. Father what grace!
Raising us to life, choosing us in Christ;
Father, what grace!

Deep is the joy that fills your courts above,
while angels wonder at your redeeming love:
and as you gaze with joy upon your Son,
your eyes are on the ones his love has won.

No higher call than to be heirs with him,
so let our passion burn for heavenly things:
seated with Christ, for him alone to live,
our hearts forever where our treasure is.

What grace! (x4)

16

GIVING IT ALL TO YOU,

giving it all to you,
no more hidden agenda,
giving it all to you.

Laying my burdens down,
bowing in full surrender,
kneeling before your cross, giving it all to you.

17

GOD, YOU'RE MY GOD, YOU'RE MY GOD

God, you're my God, you're my God.
And I will seek you, yes, I will seek you. (x2)

You satisfy my soul (x2)
so I will praise you as long as I live (x2)

I've seen your power and your glory
you've let me see you in the sanctuary:
because your love is better than my life,
I will lift up my hands in sacrifice.

We give you praise, give you praise. (x2)
For you are worthy, yes, you are worthy (x2)

So I will praise you as long as I live (x2)

17a Sanctus and Beatus quivenit

Holy, holy, holy Lord,
God of power and might,
heaven and earth are full of your glory.
Hosanna in the highest.

Blessed is he who comes in the name
of the Lord.
Hosanna in the highest.

From Common Worship:
Services and Prayers for the Church of England

18
GOD IS OUR FATHER
in heaven above,
and he cares for his children with infinite love.
Our worries are needless,
look up in the sky
where carefree and singing the birds freely fly.

Their maker who knows them,
supplies all their food,
how much more is our Father
concerned for our good.

For our Father in heaven knows all of our needs,
he will care for us always, we surrender our all,
and make the kingdom of heaven our goal.

Look at the lilies
and see how they grow:
they are clothed by God's goodness
in beautiful show.
Our Father in heaven
who cares for each flower,
provides for us always so great is his power.

For our Father in heaven ...

The kingdom of heaven
and his righteousness
we will seek with a passion
so all may be blessed.

David Lyle Morris and Nick Wynne-Jones
Copyright © 2000 Kingsway's Thankyou Music

19
GOD OF THE MOUNTAINS
God of the sea,
God of the heavens, of eternity
God of the future,
God of the past,
God of the present,
God of all history.

Creation praise will thunder to you,
thunder to you, thunder to you.
Creation praise will thunder to you,
I'm lost in the wonder,
lost in the wonder of you.

Wisdom of ages,
light in the dark,
home for the outcast,
peace for the heart:
friend of the lonely,
strength for oppressed,
voice of the voiceless,
God of all liberty.

Sue Rinaldi, Caroline Bonnett & Steve Bassett
Copyright © 2001 Kingsway's Thankyou Music

20
GRACE AND MERCY
wash over me,
cleanse my soul with your healing stream.
Here I stand with this prayer within my heart;
take me deeper in the river
that flows with your love.

Thank you, thank you:
O what riches are mine in Christ Jesus.
Thank you, thank you:
your forgiveness is so undeserved.

Grace and mercy ...

Dave Bilbrough
Copyright 2000 Kingsway's Thankyou Music

20a Open our lips

Leader: O Lord, open our lips
All: **and our mouth shall proclaim**
          your praise

Leader: Give us the joy of your saving help
All: **and sustain us with your**
          life-giving Spirit.

From Common Worship:
Services and Prayers for the Church of England

21
HAVE COURAGE AND WAIT
have courage and wait,
wait for the Lord, have courage and wait.
Have courage and wait, have courage and wait,
wait for the Lord,

Men: have courage and wait,
Women: have courage, have courage and wait

Confess every sin, confess every sin,
all of our sins, confess them to him.
Confess every sin, confess every sin,
all of our sins,

Men: confess them to him.
Women: confess them, confess them to him.

Encircle us Lord, encircle us Lord,
circle us Lord and shield us from harm.
Encircle us Lord, encircle us Lord
circle us Lord,

Men: and shield us from harm.
Women: shield us, and shield us from harm.

Lord lighten our way, Lord lighten our way,
carry our load, Lord, lighten our way.
Lord lighten our way, Lord lighten our way,
carry our load,

Men: Lord lighten our way,
Women: Lord lighten, Lord lighten our way.

O keep me true, O keep me true,
keep me true, Lord only to you.
O keep me true, O keep me true,
O keep me true,

Men: Only to you.
Women: Lord only, Lord only to you.

Jill Sutheran
Copyright © 1997 Jill Sutheran/Northumbria Community Trust

22
HE HAS COME
to bring light into the darkness;
he has come to bring freedom to the captives;
he has come to restore the broken-hearted,
it's time to proclaim the year of the Lord.

Prepare the way (prepare the way)
prepare the way for our Redeemer;
prepare the way (prepare the way)
prepare the way for our Restorer.

All: Make ready your heart, make ready your home
make ready the people of God
prepare the way.

He has come to bring hope to the hopeless;
he has come to comfort all who mourn;
he has come to heal our every sickness,
it's time to proclaim the year of the Lord.

Darrell Evans & Eric Nuzum. Copyright © 2000
Integrity's Hosanna! Music/Adm. by Kingsway's Thankyou Music

22a After Communion Prayer (1)

Almighty God,
we thank you for feeding us
with the body and blood
  of your Son Jesus Christ.
Through him we offer you our souls
and bodies to be a living sacrifice.
Send us out in the power of your Spirit
to live and work to your praise and glory.
Amen.

From Common Worship:
Services and Prayers for the Church of England

23
HERE IN YOUR ARMS
I am lost in your love.
Holding me close,
never let me fall

I will worship you (x2)
Oh, I will worship you, Lord.

Here face to face,
I am lost in praise.
Love's hunger grows,
burning stronger still.

Ken Riley
Copyright © 1999 Kingsway's Thankyou Music

23a Veni Creator

Come Lord, come down,
Come in, come among us.
Come as the wind to move us;
Come as the light to prove us;
Come as the night to rest us;
Come as the sun to warm us;
Come as the stillness to calm us;
Come Lord, come down,
Come in, come among us.

© *David Adam (Used as a Harvest prayer in Celtic Daily Prayer)*
© *Northumbria Community Trust Ltd. Tel: 01289 388235*

24
HEAR OUR PRAYER
we are your children,
and we've gathered here today.
We've gathered here to pray.
Hear our cry, Lord,
we need your mercy,
and we need your grace today,
hear us as we pray.

continued over...

Our Father, who art in heaven,
hallowed be thy name.
Our Father, hear us from heaven,
forgive our sins, we pray.

Hear our song as it rises to heaven,
may your glory fill the earth
as the waters cover the sea.
See our hearts and remove anything
that is standing in the way
of coming to you today.

Our Father ...

And though we are few we're surrounded by many
who have crossed that river before
and this is the song we'll be singing forever:
holy is the Lord, holy is the Lord (x2)

Hear our prayer ...

Our Father ...

24a The Lord's Prayer
From Matthew 6:9–13

As our Saviour has taught us, so we pray:
Our Father in heaven,
hallowed be your name,
your kingdom come,
your will be done
on earth as in heaven.
Give us today our daily bread.
Forgive us our sins,
as we forgive those who sin against us.
Lead us not into temptation,
but deliver us from evil.
For the kingdom, the power and the
glory are yours, now and forever,
Amen.

25
HOLY, HOLY

is the Lord our God;
who was and is and is to come,
and evermore shall be.

With a grateful heart
I will give my praise
to the Lamb upon the throne;
King of ages, Lord of life,
exalted over all.

26
HOLY, HOLY

holy, holy is the Lord God Almighty
holy, holy, holy, holy
is the song around the throne.
Where the angels and the elders
gather there in sweet assembly
singing holy, singing holy is the Lord our God.

Worthy, worthy, worthy, worthy
is the Lamb who was slain for me:
worthy, worthy, worthy, worthy,
is the song within my heart.
I could choose to spend eternity
with this my sole refrain,
singing worthy, singing worthy
is the Lord our God.

The way, the truth, the life,
the light, the King, the great I Am.
My life, my all, my ev'ry breath,
the Rock on which I stand.

Oh Jesus, oh Jesus,
how you suffered and died for us:
oh Jesus, oh Jesus,
but that tomb is empty now.
And I long to gaze upon your throne
and all your risen glory:
singing Jesus, singing Jesus is the Lord of all.

The way, the truth, the life ...

Holy, holy, holy, holy is the Lord God Almighty,
singing holy, singing holy is the Lord our God.

27
HOLY ONE

righteous King, merciful you are:
merciful I'll be.
Broken one, bruised for me,
in your death, O Lord,
you have set me free.

Because your Father loved me so
you came to me, Lord Jesus,
so that I would know
love unconditional and life eternal,
oh my Lord, my God, my all.

Risen One, Majesty, restoration,
come breathe new life in me.
(Repeat)

27a A Meditation
Based on Matthew 20:29–34

You stop for those whom others would silence,
and in their desperation you hear faith.
You open eyes to see and hearts to follow,
for your love is mercy
and your touch heals us all.

© P Sheppy

28
HOPE HAS FOUND ITS HOME

within me, now that I've been found in you.
Let all I am be all you want me to be,
'cause all I want is more of you,
all I want is more of you.

Let your presence fall upon us,
I want to see you face to face;
let me live forever lost in your love,
'cause all I want is more of you,
all I want is more of you.

I'm living for this cause,
I lay down my life into your hands
I'm living for the truth, the hope of the world,
in you I'll stand. All I want is you.

... All I want is,
all I want is you Jesus.

Joel Houston. Copyright © 2000
Joel Houston/Hillsong Publishing/Kingsway's Thankyou Music

28a Knowing Jesus
Philippians 3:8

What is more, I consider everything a
loss compared to the surpassing greatness
of knowing Christ Jesus my Lord,
for whose sake I have lost all things.

29
HOVER O'ER ME

Holy Spirit, bathe my trembling heart and brow;
fill me with thy hallowed presence,
come, O come and fill me now.

Thou can fill me gracious Spirit,
though I cannot tell thee how;
but I need thee greatly need thee,
come, O come and fill me now.

Fill me now, fill me now
Jesus, come and fill me now.
Fill me with thy hallowed presence,
Jesus, come and fill me now.

I am weakness, full of weakness,
at thy sacred feet I bow;
blest, divine, eternal Spirit,
come with power and fill me now.

Elwood R. Stokes (1879)

30
HOW CAN I REPAY YOU

Lord, for all you've done for me?
Nothing I can say or do
will ever be enough.

I will live for you, walking in your way,
lifting high your name, holding close the cross.
Not in words alone, but in what I do;
I will live my life for you.

Dear Lord, your heart is drawing me,
a calling from your throne.
And in my brokenness, I come
and whisper to you Lord.

It's not by works, but by your grace,
I'll never earn your love.
You loved me first, you'll love me last,
your cross my only hope.

Geraldine Latty
Copyright © 2000 Kingsway's Thankyou Music

30a Rest for your souls
Matthew 11:28–30

'Come to me, all you who are weary
and burdened, and I will give you rest.
Take my yoke upon you and learn from me,
for I am gentle and humble in heart,
and you will find rest for your souls.
For my yoke is easy and my burden is light.'

31
I AM AMAZED

by the power of your grace,
I am amazed that you took my sin and shame;
restoring hope, restoring dignity:
your grace covers me.

I'm overwhelmed by your love and goodness,
I'm overwhelmed that you took my brokenness:
amazing love, how can this be?
Your grace covers me, your grace covers me.

Saving grace, washing over me;
saving grace, that made a way for me:
I was lost until you rescued me,
your grace covers me.

Lara Martin
Copyright © 2001 Lara Martin/Abundant Life Ministries

31a Ask, Seek, Knock
From Matthew 7:7–11

What does the Father long to give?
He longs to give us good things.

Ask
and it will be given to you.
Seek
and you will find.
Knock
and the door will be opened.

For everyone who asks
receives!
Everyone who seeks
finds!
And to everyone who knocks
the door is opened!

What does the Father long to give?
He longs to give us good things.

© Mark Earey

32a Prayer of humble access

Most merciful Lord,
your love compels us to come in.
Our hands were unclean,
our hearts were unprepared;
we were not fit even to eat the crumbs
from under your table.
But you, Lord, are the God of our salvation,
and share your bread with sinners.
So cleanse and feed us with the precious
body and blood of your Son,
that he may live in us and we in him;
and that we, with the whole company of
Christ, may sit and eat in your kingdom.
Amen.

From Common Worship:
Services and Prayers for the Church of England

32
I CAN FEEL YOUR ARMS

surrounding, treasuring my soul.
Draw me ever closer into your love,
into your love.
Lead me to your place of wonder,
shower me with grace.
Holy God, forgive my unrighteous ways,
unrighteous ways.

Oh I love you Lord, all I am is yours,
as your mercy pours into my heart.
You're my faithful King, over everything,
hear my spirit sing that Jesus is Lord.

Ken Riley
Copyright © 1995 McKenzie Music/Kingsway's Thankyou Music

33
I COME TO YOU

Lord of all hope,
giver of life, revive my soul.
I wait for you, Prince of all peace,
King of all love, draw near to me.

It feels sometimes like you're far away,
yet I know you are with me.

And I know I cannot go from your presence,
O Lord, but I need to feel you here with me.
What can I do just to draw near to you?
Oh, I need to know you here with me now.

Come to me now, Lord of my heart,
I need to know unfailing love.
Consuming flame, passion and power,
come let your fire burn in me now.

It feels sometimes ...

And I know I cannot go ...

Where can I go just to find you, O God?
Oh, I long to feel you holding me.
Know that I seek you with all of my heart.
Oh, I need to find you here with me now.

Matt Parker and Paul Oakley
Copyright © 1999 Kingsway's Thankyou Music

34
I FIX MY EYES ON YOU

on the things unseen,
on the things above, on eternity.
I set my mind on you, who endured the cross,
scorning all the shame, to rescue me.
Oh, to be with you, shed this mortal skin.

I live my life for you, as I walk by faith
in the works you have prepared for me.
I run this race for you, as I set my gaze
on the greatest prize there could ever be.
Oh, to gaze on you, shed this mortal skin.

For you, for you, for you,
for you, for you, Jesus!

I'll be a fool for you, as I carry the cross
help me walk in love and purity.
So let your light shine through.

Never let this clay ever hide the light
you've given me.
Let your light shine through,
through this mortal skin.

For you, for you, for you ...

35
IF I RISE

on the wings of the dawn;
if I rest on the far side of the sea;
even there your arms will keep me warm;
even there your loving hand is sure to guide me.

From your Spirit where can I go?
From your presence where can I flee?
You are there in the ocean far below;
I go up to the heavens, you are there beside me.

You have searched and you see
all of me, all of me.
I will give willingly
all of me, all of me.

36
IF WE CALL TO HIM

he will answer us;
if we run to him, he will run to us;
if we lift our hands, he will lift us up;
come now praise his name
all you saints of God.

O sing for joy to God, our strength;
O sing for joy to God, our strength,
our strength.

Draw near to him, he is here with us;
give him your love, he's in love with us;
he will heal our hearts,
he will cleanse our hands;
if we rend our hearts,
he will heal our land.

36a The Lord requires
Micah 6:8

He has showed you, O man, what is good.
And what does the Lord require of you?

To act justly and to love mercy
and to walk humbly with your God.

37
I HAVE COME TO LOVE YOU

for you have won my heart
when you revealed your love to me.
My life will be a witness
of such love and such forgiveness,
for you have given me your peace,
and you're ev'rything I need.

I love to sing your name,
to speak about your fame,
you're worthy of my praise.
I long to worship you
in spirit and in truth,
it's all I want to do.

You have come to love me
and heal my broken heart,
now I am reaching out to you.
Your strength is in my weakness,
I'm clinging to your promise,
so let your work in me shine through
in everything I do.

As I come before you now,
let your Spirit touch me;
I will make this gospel known.
Fill me with your love and power
and your compassion,
through me let your kingdom come.

37a Comfort for the thirsty
Isaiah 55:3a

Give ear and come to me;
hear me, that your soul may live.

38
I HAVE HEARD

so many songs, listened to a thousand tongues,
but there is one that sounds above them all.

The Father's song, the Father's love,
you sung it over me and for eternity
it's written on my heart.

Heaven's perfect melody,
the Creator's symphony,
you are singing over me the Father's song.

Heaven's perfect mystery,
the King of love has sent for me,
and now you're singing over me the Father's song.

38a The compassion of Christ
From Matthew 20:37

Loving Lord,
let us feel the touch that restores,
and help us to give the touch
that speaks of your love,
that we may know the compassion
of Christ in our lives
and others may know it in meeting us.
Amen

© Mark Earey

39
I JUST WANT TO LOVE

I just want to sing to the One above
who has touched this thirsty soul.
(Repeat)
And now I'll never be the same.

I'll always love you,
I'll always sing to you, Jesus.
I long to worship you in spirit and in truth.

Every day I'll come, spend my life with you,
learning of your heart,
and what you're calling me to do.
(Repeat)
My every breath belongs to you.

And with this song
we'll lift the name of Jesus higher.
And with a shout we'll raise up one voice.

Tim Hughes
Copyright © 1998 Kingsway's Thankyou Music

40
I LIFT MY EYES TO YOU

eyes that have seen a thing or two:
who is this stranger in my life?
I lift my eyes to you,
hands that have carried what is true,
Intimate stranger be my life.

And Jesus I love you, Jesus I adore you,
Jesus, you still have my affection,
and my song will be 'I love you'.

I lift my voice to you,
lips that have cried a prayer or two;
beautiful stranger fill my life.
I lift my heart in praise to
the Saviour whose death made all things new.
Intimate stranger only you.

Martin Smith. Copyright © 2000
Curious? Music UK/Adm. by Kingsway's Thankyou Music

40a Extract from 'Do you know him?'

The Bible says my God is:

The greatest phenomenon that has ever
crossed the horizon of this world.
He's God's Son.
He's the sinner's Saviour.
He's the centrepiece of civilisation.
He stands in the solitude of himself.
He's honest and he's unique.
He's unparalleled.
He's unprecedented.
He is the loftiest idea in literature.
He's the highest personality in philosophy.
He is the supreme problem
in higher criticism.
He's the fundamental doctrine of sociology.
He is the necessity for spiritual religion.
He's the miracle of the age.
He's the superlative of everything good
that you'd please to call him.
He's the only one who qualifies
to be an all-sufficient Saviour.
I wonder, do you know him today?

Dr Loughridge (source unknown).

41
I'M GIVING YOU MY HEART

and all that is within
I lay it all down for the sake of you my King.
I'm giving you my dreams,
I'm laying down my rights
I'm giving up my pride for the promise of new life.

And I surrender
all to you, all to you.

I'm singing you this song, I'm waiting at the cross,
and all the world holds dear, I count it all as loss.
For the sake of knowing you,
the glory of your name
to know the lasting joy, even sharing in your pain.

Marc James
Copyright © 2000 Vineyard Music (UK/Eire) admin. by CopyCare

41a Life in the kingdom
Matthew 6:33

But seek first his kingdom and his
righteousness, and all these things will be
given to you as well.

42

I'M ON MY KNEES

at the cross, where your blood was sacrificed;
so amazed that there is
grace enough for me.
I don't deserve the love you bring
but I'm at that place again
where I need you
to forgive my foolish heart.

Oh what mercy,
Oh what mercy,
Oh what mercy is mine to receive.

I'm on my knees at the cross,
where your blood was sacrificed;
so amazed that there is
grace enough for me.

Dave Bilbrough
Copyright 2000 Kingsway's Thankyou Music

42a Calling on the Spirit of God

Be with us, Spirit of God;
nothing can separate us from your love.

Breathe on us, breath of God;
fill us with your saving power.

Speak in us, wisdom of God;
bring strength, healing and peace.

From Common Worship:
Services and Prayers for the Church of England

43

IN AWE OF YOU WE WORSHIP

and stand amazed at your great love.
We're changed from glory to glory,
we set our hearts on you, our God.

Now your presence fills this place,
be exalted in our praise.
As we worship I believe you are near.
(Repeat)

Blessing and honour and glory and power
forever, forever.
(x8)

In awe of you we worship.

Reuben Morgan. Copyright © 1999
Reuben Morgan/Hillsong Publishing/Kingsway's Thankyou Music

44

I SEE THE LORD

and he is high and lifted up,
and his train fills the temple.
I see you, Lord,
and you are high and lifted up,
and your train fills the temple.

And I cry holy, holy is the Lord,
holy is the Lord most high.
And I cry holy, holy is the Lord,
holy is the Lord most high.

I see your holiness
and light surrounds your throne.
Who am I to come before you?
But now my guilt is gone,
my sins are washed away,
through your blood I come.

Who am I that I should
gain the Father's love?
Now my eyes have seen the King.
Touch my lips that I may
tell of all you've done;
fill my heart I cry, be glorified!

I see the Lord ...

And I cry holy ...

Paul Oakley
Copyright © 1999 Kingsway's Thankyou Music

44a After Communion Prayer (2)

Father of all, we give you thanks and praise,
that when we were still far off
you met us in your Son and brought us home.
Dying and living, he declared your love,
gave us grace, and opened the gate of glory.
May we who share Christ's body
  live his risen life;
we who drink his cup bring life to others;
we whom the Spirit lights
  give light to the world.
Keep us firm in the hope you have
  set before us,
so we and all your children shall be free,
and the whole earth live to praise your name;
through Christ our Lord.
Amen.

From Common Worship:
Services and Prayers for the Church of England

45
IT IS GOOD, IT IS GOOD, IT IS GOOD
to give thanks to the Lord on high,
to sing of your faithfulness
and loving kindness both day and night;
to play on our instruments
sweet songs of praise for the things you do.
It is good, it is good,
it is good to give thanks to you.

For though the wicked
spring up like the grass and are everywhere,
soon they will perish;
but all those planted in your house
will grow without end. Sing it again...

For though we struggle
and trials and troubles still come our way,
you won't forsake us;
your word has told us
your promises will never end. Sing it again...

Leader: Why give him praise?
All: Because he is worthy.
Leader: Why should we sing?
All: He loves you and me.
Leader: Why give him thanks?
All: Because he forgave us.
Leader: Why celebrate?
All: Because we are free.

Leader: And when should we thank him?
All: In morning and evening.
Leader: In what circumstance?
All: The good and the bad.
Leader: Is it always easy?
All: No, it's not so easy.
Leader: But is it good?
All: Yes it's good, it is good it is good

45a Praise the Lord
Psalm 103:1

Praise the Lord, O my soul;
all my inmost being, praise his holy name.

46
I'VE THROWN IT ALL AWAY
that I might gain a life in you.
I've found all else is loss
compared to the joys of knowing you.
Your beauty and your majesty
are far beyond compare;
you've won my heart, now this will be my prayer.

'Take the world but give me Jesus!'
You're the treasure in this life.
'Take the world but give me Jesus!' is my cry.
Now I've seen you as the Saviour,
I will leave the rest behind:
'Take the world but give me Jesus!' is my cry.

Into the world I'll go
that I might live this life of love.
I won't be overcome,
for you are in me and you are strong.
For time and for eternity
I know I'm in your care;
you've won my heart,
now this will be my prayer.

... 'Take the world but give me Jesus!' is my cry.

47
JESUS ENTHRONED FOREVER
and the fame of his name
endures through every generation.
Jesus enthroned forever,
yes he reigns, we proclaim, he is Lord.

He holds the keys of freedom for the pris'ner,
he has defeated every spirit of death,
he is the strong and mighty Deliverer,
he brings peace where there is distress.

And every soul he loves with such passion,
there is nobody escaping his love.
There is a cross, now empty but still standing
where there flows the power of his blood.

Jesus enthroned forever ...

48
JESUS, GOD TO THE RESCUE
Jesus, God with us.
Jesus, name of the Saviour,
mighty Deliverer,
come, Jesus come!
Come, Lord come!
Come, Lord come!
Come, Lord come!

Come to every circumstance
that we place in your hands
whether we fly or if we fall.
We need your saving grace
at every hour and place
there is no higher name to call.

Come, and heal the broken lives,
put hope back in their eyes
we long to see the bound released.
Come Spirit of the Lord,
pour out the oil of joy
in this year of jubilee.

Come, and touch your church again
with your empowering
whether we're high or if we're low.
It's at the cross we meet
the place that we agree
only one faith, one church, one Lord.

Godfrey Birtell.
Copyright © 1999 Radical UK Music/Sovereign Music UK

49
JESUS CHRIST IS WAITING
waiting in the streets;
no one is his neighbour,
all alone he eats.
Listen, Lord Jesus,
I am lonely too:
make me, friend or stranger,
fit to wait on you.

Jesus Christ is raging,
raging in the streets,
where injustice spirals
and real hope retreats.
Listen, Lord Jesus,
I am angry too:
in the kingdom's causes
let me rage with you.

Jesus Christ is healing,
healing in the streets,
curing those who suffer,
touching those he greets.
Listen, Lord Jesus,
I have pity too:
let my care be active,
healing just like you.

Jesus Christ is dancing,
dancing in the streets,
where each sign of hatred
he, with love, defeats.
Listen, Lord Jesus,
I should triumph too;
where good conquers evil
let me dance with you.

Jesus Christ is calling,
calling in the streets,
'Who will join my journey?
I will guide their feet.'

Listen, Lord Jesus,
let my fears be few:
walk one step before me;
I will follow you.

Words: The Iona Community
Copyright © 1998,1997 WGRG, Iona Community

50
JESUS MELT MY COLD HEART
break my stony emotions.
'Cos I've been playing with the waves
when I should be swimming in the ocean.
(Repeat)

Take me deeper, show me more.
It's all or nothing, I give you everything, my Lord.

Jesus show your mercy,
I'm so sorry for waiting.
I should be running to your heart
but I know I've been hesitating.

Caroline Bonnett & Steve Bassett
Copyright © 2001 Kingsway's Thankyou Music

51
JESUS, NAME ABOVE ALL NAMES
my soul cries Jesus, it's the sweetest song.
Jesus, echoing throughout all of the heavens,
angelic hosts proclaim.

Morning star, rising sun, lily of the valleys
rose of Sharon, Son of God.
Lifted up, glorified, praised through all the ages:
the first and last, beginning and end.

Owen Hurter
Copyright © 2000 Kingsway's Thankyou Music

51a The Son, the image of God
Hebrews 1:1–4

In the past God spoke to our forebears
through the prophets at many times and in
various ways, but in these days he has spoken
to us by his Son, whom he appointed heir of
all things, and through whom he made the
universe.

The Son is the radiance of God's glory
and the exact representation of his being,
sustaining all things by his powerful word.
After he had provided purification for sins,
he sat down at the right hand of the Majesty
in heaven. So he became as much superior
to the angels as the name he has inherited is
superior to theirs.

52
JINA LA YESU LIBARIKIWE
Jina la Yesu libarikiwe,
Jina la Yesu libarikiwe,
Jina la nguvu zote.

Bless that wonderful name of Jesus, (x3)
no other name I know.

Traditional Kenyan

52a A Declaration of Praise

Leader: Praise the Lord! King of Kings.
All: We come before Him with singing.
Leader: Praise the Lord! King of Creation.
All: We come before Him in wonder.
Leader: Praise the Lord! King of Love.
All: We come before Him with thanks.
Leader: Praise the Lord! King Jesus.
All: We come before Him as an offering.

© 2000 Fiona Williamson

53
KEEP ME AS THE APPLE OF YOUR EYE.
Hide me in the shadow of your wings.

And I will see you in your glory,
I will see you as you are,
and I will see you in your beauty,
and I, I will be satisfied.

Jessica Colacuori
Copyright © 2000 Declaration Music

54
KING OF LOVE
praise you, King of love worship you,
King of love thank you,
I'm treasure in your eyes.
(Repeat)

I know my heart will love you forever,
I know your word, I'll always be your child.
I know my soul is safe for eternity
'cos you hold me close in your arms.

Gonna give you all the praise I can,
gonna give you all the thanks I can,
in your arms I will be,
King of love holding me.
Gonna give you all the love I can,
gonna give you all the praise I can.

King of love, King of love, I worship you.

Doug Horley
Copyright © 1999 Kingsway's Thankyou Music

55
KING OF OUR LIVES
your favour rests
on all who know their need of God,
and you will comfort those who mourn.
The humble meek possess the earth,
your mighty word turns upside down
all that this world considers great.

Jesus, King of our lives, as once they came
to hear your life-sustaining words,
we gather now with hungry hearts
your living truth alone can fill.

King of our lives, the pure in heart
will know the joy of seeing God,
so purify us deep within:
our thoughts, our words, the things we do;
your searching word turns inside out –
so touch our hearts and make us clean.

Jesus, we come, sit at your feet,
yield you our lives, that we may be salt of the earth,
light of the world.
All of our cares we give to you,
all that we need our Father gives,
so we will put your kingdom first.

King of our lives, as once they came
to hear your life-transforming word
we ask you now to rule our hearts
with living words, to do your will.

King of our lives, Teacher.
Rule in our hearts, Saviour.
King of our lives, Messiah.
Rule in our hearts, Master, Healer and friend.

David Lyle Morris & Nick Wynne-Jones
Copyright © 2000 Kingsway's Thankyou Music

55a Prayer of preparation

Almighty God,
to whom all hearts are open,
all desires known,
and from whom no secrets are hidden:
cleanse the thoughts of our hearts
by the inspiration of your Holy Spirit,
that we may perfectly love you,
and worthily magnify your holy name;
through Christ our Lord.
Amen.

From Common Worship:
Services and Prayers for the Church of England

56
LIGHT OF THE WORLD
you stepped down into darkness,
open my eyes, let me see.
Beauty that made this heart adore you,
hope of a life spent with you.

So here I am to worship,
here I am to bow down,
here I am to say that you're my God,
you're altogether lovely,
altogether worthy,
altogether wonderful to me.

King of all days, oh so highly exalted,
glorious in heaven above,
humbly you came to the earth you created,
all for love's sake became poor.

And I'll never know how much it cost
to see my sin upon that cross.
(Repeat)

Tim Hughes
Copyright © 2000 Kingsway's Thankyou Music

56a Declaration of faith

To whom shall we go? You have the words
of eternal life,
and we have believed and have come to know
that You are the Holy One of God.

Praise to You, Lord Jesus Christ,
King of endless glory.

Part of Morning Prayer from Celtic Daily Prayer
© Northumbria Community Trust Ltd. Tel: 01289 388235

57
LOOK WHAT YOU'VE DONE
in my life,
see what you've done in this heart,
you've brought hope, healing and freedom,
look what you've done in my life.
(Repeat)

And though I'm not deserving of your love,
you give it all to me,
with open arms you welcome me.

Your love is higher that the mountains,
your love is deeper than the sea,
Jesus, you came to pay my ransom,
it's your love, Jesus, that sets me free.

Eoghan Heaslip & Mick Goss
Copyright © 1999 Daybreak Music Ltd

57a Opening prayer

Faithful one, whose word is life:
come with saving power to free our praise,
inspire our prayer and shape our lives
for the kingdom of your Son,
Jesus Christ our Lord.
Amen

© Christopher Cocksworth

58
LORD, WE TURN TO YOU AND PRAY
we come to seek your face,
to call upon your name.
So Lord, open up the doors,
the floodgates of your love,
Lord we pray that you'd reveal your glory.

For oh, that the heavens would rend and be opened
and you, you would come down.
The mountains would tremble,
our hearts would be humbled before you.

Open up the heavens, Lord,
and shower down with your love,
pour out your presence on us, we pray,
that you would come and heal our land,
let your love flood our barrenness,
pour out your presence on us, we pray,
Lord, we pray.

Eoghan Heaslip, Mick Goss & Becky Heaslip
Copyright © 2000 Daybreak Music Ltd

59
LORD, YOUR MERCY
overwhelms me,
and your goodness amazes me;
you are loving, like a mother
and forgiving like no other.

What shall I say? What can I do?
What sacrifice
can show I'm grateful? (x2)

All I can do is worship you, Lord,
your grace is enough to keep me O God.
All that I have,
and all that I am, I pour out to you.

Your forgiveness brings me cleansing
and your healing releases me;
you are faithful like a father,
and believe in me like no other will.

Russ Hughes.
Copyright © Joshua Music/Alliance Media Ltd admin. by CopyCare

59a Life with Jesus
Mark 8:35

... whoever wants to save his life will lose it, but whoever loses his life for me and for the gospel will save it.

60
MERCY

mercy, Lord,
your mercy is how we are restored;
mercy, O mercy Lord,
help us to show your mercy, Lord.

You have been patient with our offences,
you have forgiven all of our sins;
we were deserving only your judgement,
but your great mercy triumphed again.

Lord, you have taught us 'love one another',
as you have loved us, so we must love;
always forbearing, always forgiving,
showing to others the mercy we've known.

Lynn DeShazo & Gary Sadler. Copyright © 1997
Integrity's Hosanna! Music/Adm. by Kingsway's Thankyou Music

60a Perfect love
Matthew 5:44–45

... Love your enemies and pray for those who persecute you, that you may be sons of your Father in heaven.

61
MY HOPE IS IN THE LORD

who has renewed my strength,
when everything seems senseless,
my hope is still in him.

Who has made heaven and earth
and things seen and unseen.
Whatever shade of passing day
my hope is still in him.

My hope is in the Lord. (x4)

For I know that my eyes shall see you
in the latter days to come.
When you stand on this earth
with my lips I will confess
that the hope of my heart is come (x2)

Robin Mark
Copyright © Kingsway's Thankyou Music

62
MY HOPE RESTS FIRM

on Jesus Christ, he is my only plea;
though all the world should point and scorn
his ransom leaves me free,
his ransom leaves me free.

My hope sustains me as I strive
and strain towards the goal.
Though still I stumble into sin
his death pays for it all, his death pays for it all.

My hope provides me with a spur
to help me run this race.
I know my tears will turn to joy
the day I see his face, the day I see his face.

My hope is to be with my Lord
to know as I am known;
to serve him gladly all my days
in praise before his throne,
in praise before his throne.

Keith Getty & Richard Creighton
Copyright © 2001 Kingsway's Thankyou Music

63
MY LORD, YOU WORE NO ROYAL CROWN

you did not wield the powers of state,
nor did you need a scholar's gown
or priestly robe, to make you great.

You never used a killer's sword
to end an unjust tyranny;
your only weapon was your word,
for truth alone could set us free.

You did not live a world away
in hermit's cell or desert cave,
but felt our pain and shared each day
with those you came to seek and save.

You made no mean or cunning move,
chose no unworthy compromise,
but carved a track of burning love
through tangles of deceit and lies.

You came unequalled, undeserved,
to be what we were meant to be;
to serve, instead of being served,
to pay for our perversity.

So when I stumble, set me right;
command my life as you require;
let all your gifts be my delight
and you, my Lord, my one desire.

Words: Christopher Idle
Words copyright © Christopher Idle/Jubilate Hymns

64

NAME ABOVE ALL NAMES

the Saviour for sinners slain.
You suffered for my sake,
to bring me back home again.
When I was lost, you poured your life out for me.
Name above all names, Jesus I love you.

Giver of mercy, the fountain of life for me.
My spirit is lifted to soar on the eagles' wings.
What love is this that fills my heart with treasure?
Name above all names, Jesus I love you.

High King eternal, the one true and faithful God.
The beautiful Saviour
still reigning in power and love.
With all my heart I'll worship you forever:
name above all names, Jesus I love you.

Neil Bennetts
Copyright © 2000 Daybreak Music Ltd

64a Know, Hear, Believe
From Matthew 20:29–34

Leader: Know this: The Compassionate King
accepts you,
Just as you are.
(Silence)
Hear this: The Servant King asks
you a question,
'What do you want me to do
for you?'
(Silence)

Believe this: The Listening King longs
to hear your voice!

© 2000 Jane Reeves

65

NATIONS RISE

and nations fall,
leaders come and go;
but Christ our King rules over all
and you will reign forever.

Governments and dynasties
boast of strength and power,
but you alone reign sovereignly,
you will reign forever,
our God reigns forever.

Let your kingdom come,
let your will be done,
let your kingdom come.
(Repeat)

Kings and queens leave legacies
of temporary fame;
your throne remains eternally;
you will reign forever,
our God reigns forever.

Let your kingdom come ...

One God, one Lord
one King, one Majesty;
one high, one lifted up,
one holy power.

God reigns, God reigns forever. (Repeat)
Our God reigns.

Let your kingdom come ...

Craig Smith. Copyright © 2000
Integrity's Alleluia! Music/Adm. by Kingsway's Thankyou Music

---

66

NOW IN REVERENCE AND AWE

we gather round your word;
in wonder we draw near
to mysteries that angels strain to hear,
that prophets dimly saw:
so let your Spirit
shine upon the page
and teach me;

Open up my eyes,
with truth to free me,
light to chase the lies.
Lord Jesus, let me meet you in your word;
Lord Jesus, let me meet you in your word.

Lord, your truth cannot be chained;
it searches everything –
my secrets, my desires.
Your word is like a hammer and a fire –
it breaks, it purifies:
so let your Spirit
shine into my heart
and teach me;

Graham Kendrick
Copyright © 1991 Make Way Music

66a Building on solid foundations
Matthew 7:24

Therefore everyone who hears these words of
mine and puts them into practice is like a
wise man who built his house on the rock.

67

O CHANGELESS CHRIST, FOR EVER NEW

who walked our earthly ways,
still draw our hearts as once you drew
the hearts of other days.

As once you spoke by plain and hill
or taught by shore and sea,
so be today our teacher still,
O Christ of Galilee.

As wind and storm their Master heard
and his command fulfilled,
may troubled hearts receive your word,
the tempest – tossed be stilled.

And as of old to all who prayed
your healing hand was shown,
so be your touch upon us laid,
unseen but not unknown.

In broken bread, in wine outpoured,
your new and living way
proclaim to us, O risen Lord,
O Christ of this our day.

O changeless Christ, till life is past
your blessing still be given:
then bring us home, to taste at last
the timeless joys of heaven.

Words: Timothy Dudley-Smith
Words copyright © Timothy Dudley-Smith

68

O GOD OF LOVE

I come to you again,
knowing I'll find mercy.
I can't explain all the things I see,
but I'll trust in you.
In every moment you are there,
watching over you hear my prayer.
You go before me, you're behind me,
nothing's hidden from you.

How good it is to be loved by you,
how good it is.
(Repeat)

O God of strength, your hand is on my life,
bringing peace to me.
You know my frame,
you know how I am made,
you planned all my days.
Hand of mercy, hand of love,
giving power to overcome.
If all beneath me falls away,
I know that you are God.

Who can stand against us?
In my weakness you are strong.
Your word is everlasting,
I will praise you, faithful One.

Louise & Nathan Fellingham
Copyright © 2000 Kingsway's Thankyou Music

68a A blessing

May the peace of the Lord Christ go
with you,
    wherever He may send you.
May He guide you through the wilderness,
    protect you through the storm.
May He bring you home rejoicing
    at the wonders He has shown you.
May He bring you home rejoicing
    once again into our doors.

'Peter's song for Marygate'
© Northumbria Community Trust Ltd. Tel: 01289 388235

69

O GOD, AND SPIRIT, AND JESU THE THREE

from the crown of my head, O Trinity,
to the soles of my feet mine off'ring be.
(Repeat)

Come I, with my name and my witnessing,
come I, with my contrite heart confessing,
come I unto thee, O Jesu my King.
O Jesu, Jesu, do thou be my sheltering.

O God, and Spirit ...

Words adpt. from the Cuthbert Compline in 'Celtic Daily Prayer'
Copyright © 2000 Northumbria Community Trust Ltd

69a King of Grace
From Matthew 9:9–13

I stand before you Lord
And I know I have no right
Or claim on You ...
Nothing in me that deserves Your attention.

But I know this –
You have come close
You have said my name
You have called me to follow.
Into my darkness You speak
King of Light, King of Grace.
Amazing God!

© 2000 Jane Reeves

70

O JESUS, SON OF GOD

full of grace and truth,
the Father's saving Word,
so wonderful are you.
The angels longed to see,
and prophets searched to find
the glory we have seen revealed.

You shone upon the earth
but who will understand?
You came unto your own, but who will recognise?
Your birth was prophesied,
for you were the Messiah,
who came and walked upon the earth.
You're glory we have seen, the one and only King,
and know you're living in our hearts.

Light of the world, Light of the world,
Light of the world you shine upon us.

Change us, you heal us, you free us.

In you all things were made,
and nothing without you
in heaven and on earth, all things are held in you;
and yet you became flesh, living as one of us,
under the shadow of the cross,
where through the blood you shed,
you have made peace again,
peace for the world that God so loves.

71

ONLY YOU

can replace rags for riches pure as gold,
and your mercy saved my soul,
there's none like you.

At your name demons flee,
mountains tremble in your sight,
but you love me like a friend,
there's none like you.

Nothing compares to you,
you're the one we love.
Send down your holy fire
over all the earth.
(Repeat)

You have paid such a cost,
so much more than can be won:
God, you gave your only Son,
there's none like you.

So we'll bow to the cross
where the tears of heaven fall,
you have heard the sinner's call:
there's none like you.

72

OPEN THE EYES OF MY HEART

Lord, open the eyes of my heart.
I want to see you,
I want to see you.
(Repeat)

To see you high and lifted up,
shining in the light of your glory.
Pour out your power and love,
as we sing holy, holy, holy.

Holy, holy, holy,
holy, holy, holy,
holy, holy, holy,
I want to see you.

72a Lord, you are holy
Based on Matthew 20:29–34

Leader: Lord, you are holy;
yet you have time for the blind.
Lord, you are holy:
All: **Make us holy too.**

Leader: Lord, you are holy;
yet you hear what we despise.
Lord, you are holy;
All: **Make us holy too.**

Leader: Lord, you are holy;
open our eyes to see as you see.
Lord, you are holy:
All: **Make us holy too.**

73a Priestly blessing
Numbers 6:24–26

The Lord bless you and keep you
the Lord make his face shine upon
you and be gracious to you;
the Lord turn his face towards you
and give you peace.

73
OPEN UP THE SKIES OF MERCY
rain down the cleansing flood.
Healing waters rise around us,
hear our cries, Lord, let them rise.

It's your kindness, Lord, that leads us to repentance
your favour, Lord, is our desire
and it's your beauty, Lord,
that makes us stand in silence.
your love, your love is better than life,
it's better than life.

We can feel your mercy falling,
you are turning our hearts back again,
hear our praises rise to heaven
draw us near, Lord, meet us here.

Chris Tomlin, Louie Giglio & Jesse Reeves
Copyright © 2000 worshiptogether.com songs/Six Steps Music/
EMI Christian Music Publishing admin. by CopyCare

74
PREPARE THE WAY
of the Lord, prepare the way of the Lord.
(Repeat)

Majestic in holiness, awesome in glory
doing wonders, this is our God.
We will not be silenced
from speaking his word.
We cry to the nations:

All authority is invested
in the name of Jesus,
and at the sounding of that name,
at the sounding of that name, he will arise.

Dave Bilbrough
Copyright © 2000 Kingsway's Thankyou Music

75
SACRED
holy, pure, Lord of space and time,
dwells in perfect light, radiance sublime.
Sacred holy songs rise on wings of praise,
all creation rings with echoes of your grace.

And oh my grateful heart rejoices at your name.
And oh my grateful heart rejoices at your name.

Sacred, risen Son, peerless Lamb of God;
mercy, grace and peace rolling like a flood.
Promise forged in pain,
forgiveness brought by blood,
sealed with sacred words from the mouth of God.

Sue Rinaldi, Caroline Bonnett & Steve Bassett
Copyright © 2001 Kingsway's Thankyou Music

76
SAY THE WORD
and I will sing for you;
over oceans deep I will follow.
If each star was a song,
and ev'ry breath of wind praise,
it would still fail by far
to say all my heart contains.
I simply live, I simply live for you.

As the glory of your presence now fills this place,
in worship we will meet you face to face.
There is nothing in this world
to which you can be compared
glory on glory, praise upon praise.

You bind the broken-hearted and save all my tears,
and by your word you set the captives free.
There is nothing in this world
that you cannot do:
I simply live, I simply live for you.

Russell Fragar. Copyright © 1999
Russell Frager/Hillsong Publishing/Kingsway's Thankyou Music

76a Open our lips

O Lord, open our lips
and our mouth shall proclaim your praise.
Give us the joy of your saving help
and sustain us with your life-giving Spirit.

From Common Woship:
Services and Prayers for the Church of England.

77
SPEAK THE TRUTH
in love, give to him who asks
don't quench the Spirit's fire, and love mercy.

Live a life of love, be as salt and light,
seek the Spirit's fire, and love mercy.

Think of him who died, remember how he bled,
humble now yourselves, and love mercy.

Ian White. Copyright © 1999
Little Misty Music/Kingsway's Thankyou Music

77a A Christian greeting
Jude 1b–2

To those who have been called,
who are loved by God the Father
and kept by Jesus Christ:

Mercy, peace and love
be yours in abundance.

78
TAKE ME TO YOUR SACRED PLACE
how I long to see your face.
I'll be lost in your embrace
and be loved, and be loved by you.

Take me where your glory shines,
where your holy fire burns.
Purify this heart of mine,
I surrender my life to you.

Draw me, draw me to your sacred place.
Draw me, draw me 'til I see your face.

Noel & Tricia Richards
Copyright © 2000 Kingsway's Thankyou Music

78a I Choose
From Matthew 7:24–29

Leader We have a choice
Where to put our faith.
We have a choice
Who to listen to.
We have a choice
How to live our lives.

All: **I have listened and heard**
and I choose to stand
On the only solid ground I know,
On You, O God my Rock.
Help us to sit, walk and stand
on God, our Rock,
King of the Ages.

© 2000 Jane Reeves

79
TAKE MY LIFE
and let it be consecrated, Lord, to thee;
take my moments and my days,
let them flow in ceaseless praise.

Take my hands and let them move
at the impulse of thy love,
take my feet and let them be
swift and beautiful for thee.

Take my voice and let me sing
always, only for my King:
take my lips and let them be
filled with messages from thee.

Take my silver and my gold,
not a mite would I withhold:
take my intellect and use
every power as thou shalt choose.

Take my will and make it thine
it shall be no longer mine:
take my heart, it is thine own,
it shall be thy royal throne.

Take my love, my Lord, I pour
at thy feet its treasure store:
take myself and I will be
ever, only, all for thee.

Words: Frances R Havergal (1874)

80
THANK YOU FOR THE BLOOD
that washes away my past.
Thank you for your love
that gave me a hope that will last.
Your body was broken, you died in agony,
I am so grateful you gave your life for me.

And I remember you, I remember you.
As I break this bread, and drink this wine,
I remember you.

Thank you for the blood ...

We remember you, we remember you.
As we break this bread, and drink this wine,
we remember you.

Simon Goodall. Copyright © 2000
Front2Back Records/Admin. by Daybreak Music Ltd

80a Here am I

I cannot speak, unless You loose my tongue;
I only stammer, and I speak uncertainly;
but if You touch my mouth, my Lord
then I will sing the story of Your wonders!

Here am I, my Jesus:
teach me.

Part of the Caedmon liturgy from Celtic Daily Prayer
© Northumbria Community Trust Ltd. Tel: 01289 388235

81
THE DARKEST HOUR
Lord Jesus, that rolled o'er your blest head
called forth the sweetest fragrance
that e'er on earth was shed.
That cup so full, so bitter,
the wormwood and the gall,
directly from your Father, you did accept it all.

continued over...

What perfect, meek submission!
Your will, not mine be done:
obedience full, unquestioned; perfection of a Son!
Thus prostrate there before him,
your sweat as drops of blood:
and so to be the victim, the spotless Lamb of God!

Yet you, O holy sufferer, could 'Abba, Father!' cry
through all your woe abiding
in sonship's perfect tie.
Through suffering made perfect
in heav'n our leader now
Captain of our salvation!
With reverent hearts we bow.

By this you have, Lord Jesus,
our hearts' affection gained;
how can we give you comfort
for what you have sustained?
Entire and full devotion alone can worthy be
till, love to love responsive,
your glorious face we see.

G R Cowell. Adpt by Graham Kendrick
Copyright © 2001 Make Way Music

81a A Meditation and Prayer
Based on Matthew 20:20–28

'Can you drink the cup?' you ask.
And to your right and left
two dying thieves drink the cup of death.
In your humiliation on the cross
you reveal the greatness of love
and the hope of salvation.

Lord, you are holy;
yet you humble yourself to death.
Lord, you are holy;
Make us holy too.

Lord, you are holy;
yet you bear human pride.
Lord, you are holy;
Make us holy too.

Lord, you are holy;
and you call us to drink your cup.
Lord, you are holy;
Make us holy too.

© P. Sheppy

82
THE PEOPLE WHO WALK IN DARKNESS
will see a great light,
for those who live in the land
of the shadow of death the light will shine.
You will enlarge the nation and increase their joy

so they delight in your presence
as they will rejoice at harvest time.

For to us a child is born, to us a Son is given
and the government will be upon his shoulders.
Of his government and peace
there will always be increase;
there is no end to his kingdom.

He will be called Wonderful, Counsellor,
Mighty God, Everlasting Father, Prince of Peace
(Repeat)
... the Prince of peace.

The people who walk in darkness...

For to us a child is born, to us a Son is given
and the government will be upon your shoulders.
Come to break our yoke of grief,
the bar across our shoulders;
Lord, smash the rod of our oppressors.

You will be called Wonderful ...

David Lyle Morris & Jussi Miettinen
Copyright © 2000 Kingsway's Thankyou Music

83
THE VOICE OF GOD
is calling with words that roar and rage;
the passion of the Father's heart
resounds through ev'ry age.
Multitudes are waiting
for this gospel we proclaim;
Christ Jesus came among us
that all men might be saved.

Show your glory, show your glory,
show your glory, over all the earth.

This is our commission,
to fill the air with praise
and to tell the people of this world
the glory of his name.
With thousands upon thousands
from every tribe and tongue
we cry 'Worthy is the Lamb' once slain
for he has overcome.

With tears of intercession,
through the prayers of all the saints,
we long to reach the nations
with humility and grace.
Come touch this generation
and use us, Lord, we pray;
fill our hearts with boldness
to do the things you say.

Dave Bilbrough
Copyright © 2000 Kingsway's Thankyou Music

83a A Prayer of Repentance

Holy God who came as a suffering servant,
forgive us for the times
   we clamour for your attention,
we demand you act in power,
we seek after signs and wonders
   for their own sake...

(Silence)

Open our eyes and our hearts
to understand that to follow you
   is to accept the path of servanthood.
In so doing we will display clearly
   the love and power of God.

(Silence)

Help me to understand what it means
to be a servant in my home,
in my family, in my work place, in my life...
Holy Spirit may the power
   that raised Jesus from death, dwell in me
to raise me to life – life in all its fullness.

To the glory of God the Father. **Amen.**

84
THERE IS A DEEPER LOVE TO KNOW

there is a higher place
where we can go.
There is a freedom at the cross,
there is a light that shines
for all the world.
And I can't hold this joy inside,
I'm jumping in your arms of mercy.

Everybody sing,
everybody shout,
for the joy of the Lord
is our strength forever.
(Repeat)

There is a brighter day to come
when all the world
will bow down to your Son.
And all the broken will rejoice
even the kings will say '
You are the Lord'
and we can't hold this joy inside
we're dancing in your arms of mercy.

84a The cross

And now we give you thanks
because, for our salvation,
he was obedient
even to death on the cross.
The tree of shame
was made the tree of glory;
and where life was lost,
there life has been restored.

85
THERE IS NO OTHER NAME

by which men can be saved,
there is no other name under heaven.
There is rest for my soul
and the wounded made whole,
and the captives set free and forgiven.
(Repeat)

Such love as I had never known,
I've found in the grace that flowed to me
in my unrighteousness;
this is why my heart and soul and tongue confess.

There is no other name ...

85a Think about it

All we like thoughts
have gone astray
Wandered off into
Strange avenues
Lost for words
Lost thoughts
Sentenced for ever.

A sentence
Not completed
Because Jesus
The Word
Found us
And completed
Our sentence.

86
THERE'S A LOT OF PAIN
but a lot more healing,
there's a lot of trouble, but a lot more peace.
There's a lot of hate, but a lot more loving,
there's a lot of sin, but a lot more grace.

Oh, outrageous grace! (x2)
Love unfurled by heavens hand
outrageous grace! (x2)
Through my Jesus I can stand.

There's a lot of fear, but a lot more freedom:
there's a lot of darkness, but a lot more light.
There's a lot of cloud, but a lot more vision:
there's a lot of perishing, but a lot more life.

There's an enemy,
that seeks to kill what it can't control.
It twists and turns,
making mountains out of molehills.
But I will call on the Lord,
who is worthy of praise;
I run to him... and I am saved!

Godfrey Birtill
Copyright © 2000 Radical UK Music/Sovereign Music UK

87
THERE'S A SONG
that everyone can sing,
there's a prayer that everyone can bring,
feel the music 'cos it's time to dance.
People all across the world,
with a heartbeat for holiness,
feel his pleasure, we are God's romance.

Hear the sound let it shake the ground,
now's the time for the saints to shine.

Everyone here is the kingdom come,
here is the God who saves the day
and we will gladly run into the glorious Son,
singing that Jesus is alive.

There's a song that everyone can sing,
there's a race that everyone can win:
leave your sadness, it's our time to dance.
Everyone let out your praise,
people with their hearts ablaze;
we've found Jesus, he's our great romance.

Hear the sound ...

Holy is the Lord (x2)

Everyone here is the kingdom come ...

Martin Smith. Copyright © 2000
Curious? Music UK/Adm. by Kingsway's Thankyou Music

88
THERE'S NO LOVE GREATER
than your love,
there's no love greater than you.
(Repeat)

I want to hear it sung around the world
that Jesus you are Lord of all.
And our praises ring that you are King
of all the heavens and the earth.
And at your name we bow,
you've turned our mourning into dancing.

I want to see the day when all will know
that Jesus you are Lord of all.
And we'll hear the songs of freedom sound
upon the lips of young and old.
And every knee shall bow
let all the earth rejoice with gladness.

You came with love, brighter than the day.
Who can deny the wonder of your name?
Don't let me fall,
I was born to be with you:
there's no love like you.

James Taylor
Copyright © 1999 Kingsway's Thankyou Music

89
THIS IS YOUR HOUSE
we are your people,
the object of your love,
purchased by your blood.
We are living stones built together to reveal
the glories of your grace.

And by your grace,
and by the power that works within us,
and by your word,
and as we daily seek you face,
we'll choose to live for you,
and die to our way,
so we can be your holy dwelling place.

Fill your house with glory,
fill your house with praise, Father.
Fill your house with prayer
for all the nations,
to your house of blessing
let the nations run,
to worship Jesus,
O, let the people come.

Graham Kendrick
Copyright © 2001 Make Way Music

90
THIS ONE DESIRE

one thing I seek,
is to be in your presence,
Lord, for all my days.
This one desire, one thing I ask,
to gaze upon your beauty, Lord,
for all my days.

I would build a bridge and cross the seas,
and climb the highest mountains,
reach for the stars, search the skies
just to be with you, just to be with you, Lord.

You are my hope and my strength,
you're all I'm living for.
You're all I need and all I seek,
you're all I'm living for, all I'm living for.

Eoghan Heaslip
Copyright © 1999 Daybreak Music Ltd

91
THOUGH TRIALS WILL COME

don't fear, don't run.
Lift up your eyes, hold fast, be strong.
Have faith, keep on believing.
Lift up your eyes for God is at work in us,
moulding and shaping us out of his love for us,
making us more like Jesus.

Consider it joy, pure joy when troubles come.
Many trials will make you strong.
Consider it joy, pure joy and stand your ground,
then at last you'll wear a crown.

Though trials will come, won't fear, won't run.
We'll lift up our eyes, hold fast, be strong.
Have faith, keep on believing.
We'll lift up our eyes for God is at work in us,
moulding and shaping us out of his love for us,
making us more like Jesus.

Consider it joy ...

Joy, pure joy, consider it joy, pure joy.
(Repeat)

Consider it joy ...

Patiently trusting him, ready for anything,
'til we're complete in him,
in everything more like Jesus.

Consider it joy ...

... then at last you'll wear a crown. (Repeat)

Graham Kendrick
Copyright © 2001 Make Way Music

91a Prayer of Recommitment
Based on Matthew 7:24–29

Leader: We have read, we have studied,
we have again considered the
teachings of Christ that everyone
who hears his words and puts them
into practice is like a wise man ...

All: We choose now to follow Jesus.
We choose now the path
of the wise man.

Leader: Thank you Lord that you are
the Maker and Sustainer of Life.
Thank you that to follow your
instructions enables us to live life
as it is intended.

All: We now pray for one another,
that in our homes, families,
churches and in our society
we may build on a sure
foundation. We accept that there
is a cost involved, that of
servanthood and suffering
but we stand looking towards
your Son ... who for the joy set
before him endured the cross.

Leader: Thank you Jesus that we are
not left to our own devices,
that you have sent us a counsellor.

All: Holy Spirit
we invite you now into our lives –
to refresh us and equip us
to follow the teachings of Jesus,
so that we might truly be salt
and light to a needy world.
Amen

© 2000 Fiona Williamson

92a Peace between me and my God

May I tread the path
to the gates of glory.
Rule this heart of mine
that it be only Yours.
God's path would I travel,
my own path refuse.
May I tread the path to the gates of glory.

Part of the Chad liturgy from Celtic Daily Prayer
© Northumbria Community Trust Ltd. Tel: 01289 388235

92
THROUGH DAYS OF RAGE AND WONDER

we pursue the end of time,
to seize the day eternal,
the reign of love divine.

Fixing our eyes on Jesus
we will press on day by day;
this world's vain passing pleasures
are not our destiny.
Our ancient rites of passage
still are the bread and wine:
our hope a cross that towers
over the wrecks of time.

Through days of rage and wonder,
by the awesome power of prayer
God will shake every nation,
secrets will be laid bare.
And if his light increasing
casts deeper shadows here,
safe in his holy presence,
love will cast out our fear.

Through days of rage and wonder,
you will give us strength to stand
and seek a heavenly city
not built by human hands.
Now is the only moment
within our power to change:
to give back in obedience
while life and breath remain.

Graham Kendrick
Copyright © 1998 Make Way Music

93
WE CALL UPON YOUR NAME

O Lord, the name that is holy.
(x4)

We call upon your name, O Lord,
we come to bring our praise to the One
who was, who is, and is to come.

Arise, King of kings,
God of all creation
O Lord we cry:
arise, King of kings,
a Father to the nations,
the Rock of our salvation,
O God arise.

Eoghan Heaslip, Mick Goss & Becky Heaslip
Copyright © 2000 Daybreak Music Ltd

94
WE CANNOT MEASURE HOW YOU HEAL

or answer every sufferer's prayer,
yet we believe your grace responds
where faith and doubt unite to care.
Your hands, though bloodied on the cross,
survive to hold and heal and warn,
to carry all through death to life
and cradle children yet unborn.

The pain that will not go away,
the guilt that clings from things long past,
the fear of what the future holds,
are present as if meant to last.
But present too is love which tends
the hurt we never hoped to find,
the private agonies inside,
the memories that haunt the mind.

So some have come who need your help
and some have come to make amends,
as hands which shaped and saved the world
are present in the touch of friends.
Lord, let your Spirit meet us here
to mend the body, mind and soul,
to disentangle peace from pain
and make your broken people whole.

Words: The Iona Community
Copyright © 1989, 1996 WGRG, Iona Community

94a Beatitudes
Matthew 5:3–10

Blessed are the poor in spirit,
for theirs is the kingdom of heaven.
Blessed are those who mourn,
for they will be comforted.
Blessed are the meek,
for they will inherit the earth.
Blessed are those who hunger and thirst
for righteousness,
for they will be filled.
Blessed are the merciful,
for they will receive mercy.
Blessed are the pure in heart,
for they will see God.
Blessed are the peacemakers,
for they will be called sons of God.
Blessed are those who are persecuted
because of righteousness,
for theirs is the kingdom of heaven.

95
WE HAVE COME
to a holy mountain,
joining angels in celebration,
a thousand, thousand lift their voices,
as the firstborn church sings her praises
to the Holy One, to the Holy One.

We've come to God the judge of all men
to those made perfect by his own Son.
A thousand, thousand lift their voices
as God's redeemed sing their praises
to the Holy Lamb, to the Holy Lamb.

O Holy God we have come to you,
consuming fire, to be refined in you.
O Holy One, how we long for you,
our one desire is found in you.

We have come to a holy mountain,
not in fear, but with rejoicing.
A thousand, thousand lift their voices
as cleansing flows through the blood of Jesus;
the Holy Lamb, the Holy Lamb.

O Holy God ...

... is found in you.

Hebrews 12: 18-28. Russ Hughes
Copyright © 2000 Joshua Music/Alliance Media admin. by CopyCare

---

96a Grace above law
Based on Matthew 5:17 and 7:1

Jesus said: 'I have not come to abolish the law
but to fulfil it.'

Merciful and gracious Lord,
make us holy, as you are holy,
and let your word and your law
be honoured and obeyed,
in our lives and in the nations.

Jesus also said: 'Do not judge, so that you
may not be judged.'

Merciful and gracious Lord,
when holiness seems but a distant vision,
in our lives and in the nations,
let grace triumph over law,
the spirit, not the letter alone,
capture our hearts,
to the glory of your name.
Amen

© Mark Earey

96
WE SEE THE LORD
and he is high upon the throne,
and his glory fills the heavens and the earth.
One like a Lamb who was slain is on the throne,
and I cast my crown before you
and bow down to praise.

For everything cries holy
O everything cries holy
O everything cries holy to you Lord.
(Repeat)

Robin Mark
Copyright © Kingsway's Thankyou Music

97
WHEN YOU PRAYED
BENEATH THE TREES
it was for me, O Lord;
when you cried upon your knees,
how could it be, O Lord?
When in blood and sweat and tears
you dismissed your final fears,
when you faced the soldiers' spears,
you stood for me, O Lord.

When their triumph looked complete,
it was for me, O Lord,
when it seemed like your defeat,
they could not see, O Lord!
When you faced the mob alone
you were silent as a stone,
and a tree became your throne;
you came for me, O Lord.

When you stumbled up the road,
you walked for me, O Lord,
when you took your deadly load,
that heavy tree, O Lord;
when they lifted you on high,
and they nailed you up to die,
and when darkness filled the sky,
it was for me, O Lord.

When you spoke with kingly power,
it was for me, O Lord,
in that dread and destined hour,
you made me free, O Lord;
earth and heaven heard you shout,
death and hell were put to rout,
for the grave could not hold out;
you are for me, O Lord.

Words: Christopher Idle
Words copyright © Christopher Idle/Jubilate Hymns.

97a Fix our eyes on Jesus
Hebrews 12:2

Let us fix our eyes on Jesus, the author
and perfecter of our faith, who for the joy
set before him endured the cross, scorning
its shame, and sat down at the right hand
of the throne of God.

98
WHITER THAN THE SNOW
purer than the clearest stream;
wash me and I'll be bathed in purity,
I long to feel clean.
A robe of righteousness,
a robe that I could not afford;
my Lord, you paid the price,
your perfect sacrifice has covered up my shame.

And so I thank you, Jesus,
for the sweet forgiveness of the cross.
It's a mystery, to amaze even angels,
that when Father looks into my heart
he sees me now as whiter than the snow.

Mike Burn
Copyright © 1998 Daybreak Music Ltd

99
WHO CAN STAND BEFORE THE LORD
in his holy place?
Who can walk upon the hill of the Lord?
Only he whose hands are clean,
only he whose heart is pure
can stand before the Lord.

I will stand, I will come
before the presence of the King
for his blood washes me from sin
I enter in.

There is one who stands for me in the holy place,
and he walked the lonely hill to the cross.
And I know his hands are clean,
and I know his heart is pure,
he is Jesus Christ the Lamb.

Psalm 24. Carey Luce and Geraldine Latty
Copyright © Carey Luce

99a Declaration of faith
We believe and trust in God the Father Almighty.
We believe and trust in Jesus Christ His Son.
We believe and trust in the Holy Spirit.
We believe and trust in the Three in One.

Part of Midday Prayer from Celtic Daily Prayer
© Northumbria Community Trust Ltd. Tel: 01289 388235

100
WHO IS THIS
that the wind and waves obey him?
Who is this, that speaks life into the dead?
Who is this, that sets the prisoner free,
makes the deaf to hear and blind to see?
Open my eyes to see again.

Who is this, with a cross upon his shoulders?
Who is this, that is mocked by those he made?
Who is this that serves upon his knees
and who gave his life to ransom me?
Open my eyes to see again.

Surely you are the Son of God,
Messiah, creation's King of love.
I turn, I trust in you.

Who is this, coming on the clouds of heaven?
Who is this, seated at the Father's side?
Who is this to whom all knees will bow,
who is given rule and sovereign power?
Open my eyes to see again.

Surely you are the Son of God ...

Now to him, O let all I am adore him.
Live for him, laying all I am before him.
Trusting like a child, serving like a slave,
taking up my cross, giving all I have.
Open my eyes to see again.

Surely you are the Son of God ...

... I turn, I trust in you.
Creation's King of love.

Copyright © Sam Chaplin

100a A prayer of trust

Lord, I believe You will make a way for me
and provide for me,
    if only I trust You and obey.
I will trust in the darkness and know
that my times are still in Your hand.
I will believe You for my future,
chapter by chapter,
    until all the story is written.
Focus my mind and my heart upon You,
my attention always on You without alteration.
Strengthen me with Your blessing
and appoint to me the task.
Teach me to live with eternity in view.
Tune my spirit to the music of heaven.

Part of the Brendan liturgy from Celtic Daily Prayer
© Northumbria Community Trust Ltd. Tel: 01289 388235

101
WHY WOULD I WORSHIP ANY OTHER?
How could I exalt another name?
There's no other who has done for me
all the things you do,
there is nothing, Lord, that compares to you,
you have captured me,
and broken the chains away.

If the rocks cry out I will sing along,
every knee will bow, I will be among them,
for the glory of my God.
When creation speaks of your mighty name,
I will join in voice and there proclaim
for the glory of my God.

Dave Chumchal. Copyright © 2001
Mercy/Vineyard Publishing admin. by CopyCare

101a The Almighty
Job 37:15–18 and 23–24

Do you know how God controls the clouds
and makes his lightning flash?
Do you know how the clouds hang poised,
those wonders of him who is perfect
in knowledge.
You who swelter in your clothes
when the land lies hushed under the
south wind,
can you join him in spreading out the skies,
hard as a mirror of cast bronze?

The Almighty is beyond our reach and
exalted in power;
in his justice and great righteousness,
he does not oppress.
Therefore, men revere him,
for does he not have regard for all the wise
in heart?

102
WORTHY, YOU ARE WORTHY
much more worthy than I've known,
I cannot imagine just how glorious you are.
I cannot begin to tell how deep a love you bring,
Lord, my ears have heard of you,
but now my eyes have seen.

You're worthy, you're worthy, you're worthy,
you're worthy to be praised,
forever and a day.
(Repeat)

Glory, I give glory to the One who saved my soul.
You found me and you freed me
from the shame that was my own.
I cannot begin to tell how merciful you've been,
Lord, my ears have heard of you,
but now my eyes have seen.

You're worthy, you're worthy, you're worthy,
you're worthy to be praised,
forever and a day.
(Repeat)

Your glory, your glory, your glory,
your glory reaches high,
so high above the heavens.
(Repeat)

Matt Redman
Copyright © 2000 Kingsway's Thankyou Music

103
YOU ARE BOUNDLESS MERCY
you are endless grace,
you are sweet forgiveness,
ceaseless faithfulness washing over me.

You are sov'reign Father, you are healing King,
you are tender Saviour,
righteous offering poured out for me.

And I surrender to you,
Lord, I'm yielding all I am to you.
You have captivated me,
and I come to give my devotion.
(Repeat)

Yes, I come to give my devotion,
O Lord, I come to give my devotion.

Kathryn Scott. Copyright © 2000
Vineyard Songs (UK/Eire) admin. by CopyCare

104
YOU ARE GOD IN HEAVEN
and here am I on earth;
so I'll let my words be few:
Jesus, I am so in love with you.

And I'll stand in awe of you,
yes, I'll stand in awe of you.
And I'll let my words be few:
Jesus, I am so in love with you.

The simplest of all love songs
I want to bring to you;
so I'll let my words be few:
Jesus, I am so in love with you.

Matt & Beth Redman
Copyright © 2000 Kingsway's Thankyou Music

104a My soul's desire

My soul's desire is to see the face
of God and to rest in His house.
My soul's desire is to study the Scriptures
and to learn the ways of God.
My soul's desire is to be freed from
all fear and sadness,
and to share Christ's risen life.
My soul's desire is to imitate my King,
and to sing His purposes always.
My soul's desire is to enter the gates of heaven
and to gaze upon the light that shines forever.

Dear Lord, You alone know
what my soul truly desires,
and You alone can satisfy those desires.

Part of the Hild liturgy from Celtic Daily Prayer
© *Northumbria Community Trust Ltd. Tel: 01289 388235*

105
YOU ARE KNOWN
as the Rock of ages
and the holy Ancient of Days.
Men of old who saw your face, Lord,
would not ever be the same.
When you came as God incarnate,
walked this earth, your glory veiled,
those who knew you, and who loved you
would not ever be the same.

For I have seen you, Rock of ages,
I will never be the same.
O, I love you, Rock of ages,
I will always love your name.

Will you hide me, Rock of ages
in your secret place of peace?
Can I feel your burning glory,
can I hear you when you speak?
Will you chasten me and mould me?
Will you hold me in your will?
O to know you, love and serve you
and your purposes fulfil.

Robin Mark
Copyright © Kingsway's Thankyou Music

106a   Towards the goal
Philippians 3:14

I press on towards the goal to win the prize
for which God has called me heavenwards in
Christ Jesus.

106
YOU ARE THE ONE I LOVE
you are the one that I adore.
(Repeat)

For you've called me by name,
drawn me close to your heart,
washed away all my shame with your tears.
For the rest of my days I will offer my life
in thanksgiving and praise to my King.

You are the one I love
you are the one that I adore.
(Repeat)

Now with you I will stay,
for your word is my light,
and your peace can allay all my fears:
and my victory song
is the song of the cross,
you have won me with love so divine.

Such precious, precious love.
You have won me with your
precious, precious love.

You are the one I love
you are the one that I adore.
(Repeat)

Sue Rinaldi & Caroline Bonnett
Copyright © 2001 Kingsway's Thankyou Music

107
YOU CAN HAVE MY WHOLE LIFE
you can come and have it all:
I don't want to go my own way now.

I love to feel your presence
and I know your saving grace,
I am nothing when you're second place.

I've been born to give you praise,
not to yearn and strive for worldly things.
I've been born to love your ways,
take my pride and let me always say:
I want to go your way now.

James Taylor
Copyright © 2000 Kingsway's Thankyou Music

107a   Love
1 John 4:19

We love because he first loved us.

108a Agnus Dei

Jesus, Lamb of God,
have mercy on us
Jesus, bearer of our sins,
have mercy on us.
Jesus, redeemer of the world,
grant us peace.

From Common Worship:
Services and Prayers for the Church of England

108b A Prayer of Dedication
Based on Matthew 5:3–9

Blessed are the poor in spirit,
for theirs is the kingdom of heaven.
Lord you are holy:
Make us holy too.

Blessed are those who mourn,
for they will be comforted.
Lord, you are holy:
Make us holy too.

Blessed are the meek,
for they will inherit the earth.
Lord, you are holy:
Make us holy too.

Blessed are those who hunger and thirst
  for righteousness,
for they will be filled.
Lord, you are holy:
Make us holy too.

Blessed are the merciful,
for they will receive mercy.
Lord, you are holy:
Make us holy too.

Blessed are the pure in heart,
for they will see God.
Lord, you are holy:
Make us holy too.

Blessed are the peacemakers,
for they will be called children of God.
Lord, you are holy:
Make us holy too.

© P Sheppy

108
YOU HAVE BEEN SO GOOD TO US

and you have not forgotten us.
Out of your great love for us,
you have taken our place
and covered us with your grace.

There was a place, there was a time
when we were guilty of a crime.
Yet willingly your love broke through
and you removed all our shame,
we can now live again.

I will dance before you early in the morning,
I will sing of your love come down
late into the night.
I will wave a banner of truth in broad daylight.
I will shout for your joy has come,
how wonderful you have been to me.

Simon Goodall
Copyright © 1998 Daybreak Music Ltd

109
YOU LED ME TO THE CROSS

and I saw your face of mercy in that place of love.
You opened up my eyes
to believe your sweet salvation,
where I'd been so blind.
Now that I'm living in your all forgiving love,
my every road leads to the cross.

Jesus, keep me near the cross,
I won't forget the love you've shown.
Saviour, teach me of the cross,
I won't forget the love,
I won't forget the love you've shown.

And there's an empty tomb,
that tells me of your resurrection and my life in you.
The stone lies rolled away, nothing but those
folded grave clothes where your body lay.
Now that I'm living as a risen child of God,
my every road leads to the cross.

Matt Redman
Copyright © 1999 Kingsway's Thankyou Music

109a   Christ died for us
Romans 5:8

... God demonstrates his own love for
us in this: While we were still sinners,
Christ died for us.

110
YOUR LIGHT

broke through my night,
restored exceeding joy.
Your grace fell like the rain,
and made this desert live.

You have turned my mourning into dancing,
you have turned my sorrow into joy.

Your hand lifted me up,
I stand on higher ground.
Your praise rose in my heart,
and made this valley sing.

You have turned ... (x2)

This is how we overcome (Repeat x7)

You turned my mourning ...

111
YOUR LOVE HAS CAPTURED ME

your grace has set me free,
your life, the air I breathe,
be glorified in me.

You set my feet to dancing,
you set my heart on fire,
in the presence of a thousand kings
you are my one desire,
and I stand before you now
with trembling hands lifted high.
Be glorified

112
YOUR LOVE IS AMAZING

steady and unchanging;
your love is a mountain, firm beneath my feet.
Your love is a mystery, how you gently lift me;
when I am surrounded, your love carries me.

Hallelujah, hallelujah,
hallelujah, your love makes me sing.
(Repeat)

Your love is surprising, I can feel it rising
all the joy that's growing deep inside of me.
Every time I see you,
all your goodness shines through
and I can feel this God song, rising up in me.

112a King of the Hill

All: My eyes look to the King of
the Hill, Clothe me with grace
and conquer my heart.

Leader: For You reign
All: You reign!

Leader: You are robed
All: In majesty!

Leader: You are armed
All: With strength!

Leader: Yes – You reign
All: You reign!

113
YOUR WHISPER TO MY SOUL

when I was like a child,
lifted off the yoke,
planted fields of hope
in this heart of mine.

You took me as I am,
you knew what I had done,
still you took my shame,
and you called my name,
I was overcome.

When you broke the bonds
of how I used to be,
you rolled away the stone,
you set the captive free.

I wanna thank you,
you're the God of mercy,
I wanna thank you God,
for giving me peace.
I wanna thank you,
you're the God who loved me,
I wanna thank you,
you're the God who rescued me.

You covered all my sin,
restored to me my youth again,
and I am satisfied,
for you have healed me and redeemed me,
crowned my head with endless beauty,
endless beauty.

I wanna thank you ...

114
YOURS IS THE KINGDOM

the power and the glory,
forever and ever,
forever and ever, amen!
(Repeat)

A trumpet blast will herald
the day of your return:
your glory and your splendour
will be seen in all the earth!
And Oh, what a day, Oh, what a day that will be,
when the earth joins with heaven
in worship and praise to Jesus!

Yours is the kingdom ...

The time is drawing nearer,
I believe it's coming soon,
when we will rise to greet you
as a bride to meet her groom.
And Oh, what a day, Oh, what a day that will be,
when the earth joins with heaven
in worship and praise to Jesus!

Yours is the kingdom ...

... Amen! Amen! Amen!

115
YOU'VE PUT A NEW SONG
in my mouth.
It is a hymn of praise to you.
Justice and mercy are its theme.
And I will live it back to you.

The kind of fast you've chosen, Lord,
it must reach out to broken lives, and to the poor.
So change me, Lord,

I know you are the orphan's hope,
I know you are the widow's song.

You're Father where no father lives
and to the lonely you're a friend,
O Lord, you're showing me what's on your heart.

You've put a new song ...

Lord, I won't bring an empty song;
it's meaningless without compassion
in my life, and holiness.

Index

Song titles differing from first lines are in italics

Index of Bible verses

Index of liturgy and prayers

Addresses of copyright holders

Abundant Life Ministries, Wapping Road, Bradford, BD3 0EQ

Bishop Timothy Dudley Smith, 9 Ashlands, Ford, Salisbury, Wiltshire, SP4 6DY

Brown Bear Music, 154 Deptford High Street, London, SE8 3PQ

CopyCare, P.O. Box 77, Hailsham, East Sussex, BN27 3EF

Daybreak Music Ltd, Silverdale Road, Eastbourne, East Sussex, BN20 7AB

Declaration Music, P.O. Box 12683, Fort Wayne, IN, 46864, USA.

I.Q. Music, Commercial House, 52 Perrymount Road, Haywards Heath, West Sussex

Jubilate Hymns, 4 Thorne Park Road, Chelston, Torquay, TQ2 6RX

Kingsway's Thankyou Music, Lottbridge Drove, Eastbourne, East Sussex, BN23 6NT

Make Way Music, P.O. Box 263, Croydon, Surrey, CR9 5AP

Northumbria Community Trust Ltd, Hetton Hall, Chatton, Northumberland, NE68 7UB

Praise Trust, P.O. Box 359, Darlington, DL3 8YD

Sovereign Music UK, PO Box 356, Leighton Buzzard, Beds., LU7 8WP

Wild Goose Resource Group, Pearce Institute, 840 Govan Road, Glasgow, G51 3UU

For a free catalogue of Spring Harvest resources

call – 01825 769000

or

click – www.springharvest.org/resources

or

email – info@springharvest.org